DATE DUE			
DEC 10	MAR 24	APR 21	
JAN 2	MAY 5		
	MAY 11		
3/10	FEB 16		
5/20	MAR 18		
SEP 29	APR 17		
FEB 3	APR 17		
OCT 11	FEB 12		
APR 21			
MAY 24	SEP 27		
JAN 28	MAY 24		
FEB 2	Mar 10		

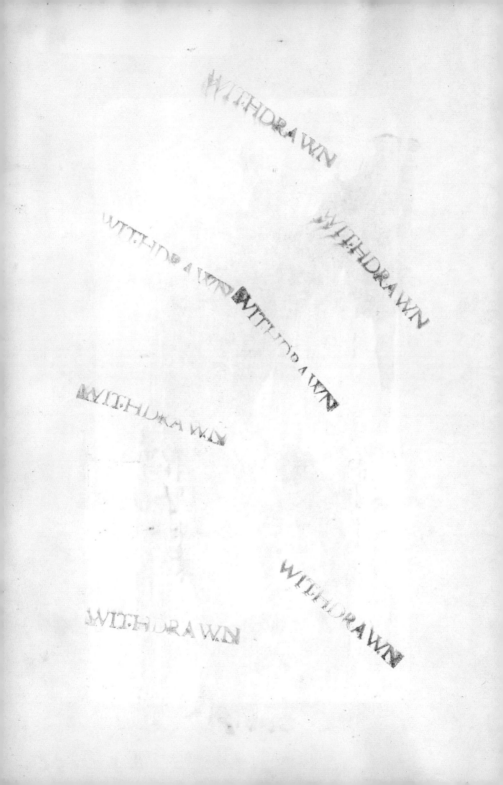

ODDITY LAND

EDWARD ANTHONY

ODDITY LAND

DRAWINGS BY

ERIK BLEGVAD

DOUBLEDAY & COMPANY, INC.

GARDEN CITY, NEW YORK

LIBRARY OF CONGRESS CATALOG CARD NUMBER 57–7275

FIXING THE BLAME

I know an Esther,
An eager suggester,
Who gave me a push and said, "Go be a jester"

Since everything's different in Oddity Land,
    I'm sure as can be that you'll understand
    That the animals there and the reptiles too
And the fish and the birds and the insect crew
Do not behave as such creatures do
In the world we know. In Oddity Land
They're a rather peculiarly mixed-up band,
Like the leopard I know whose spots are square,
And the lion who sleeps in his underwear
(He knows it's not right but he doesn't care!)—
And the tiger without any stripes on his back,
They were stolen one night while he slept, alack . . .

    But if I keep chattering on this way
    I'll completely forget that I set out to say:

I know a shark
That sings like a lark.

I know a stork
That eats with a fork.

I know a sparrow
That pushes a barrow.

I know a mosquito
Whose name is Benito.

I know a gnat
That wears a straw hat.
He uses it also for bathing his cat.

I know a lamb
That pushes a pram.

I know an ox
That always wears socks.
He's specially fond of the ones that have clocks.

9

I know a raccoon
That can whistle a tune,
But only on Tuesdays when there's a full moon.

I know a gorilla
That's fond of vanilla.

I know a turtle
Whose first name is Myrtle.

I know a linnet
That spends every minute
A-tinkling out tunes on her grandmother's spinet.

I know a duck
Who drives a big truck.

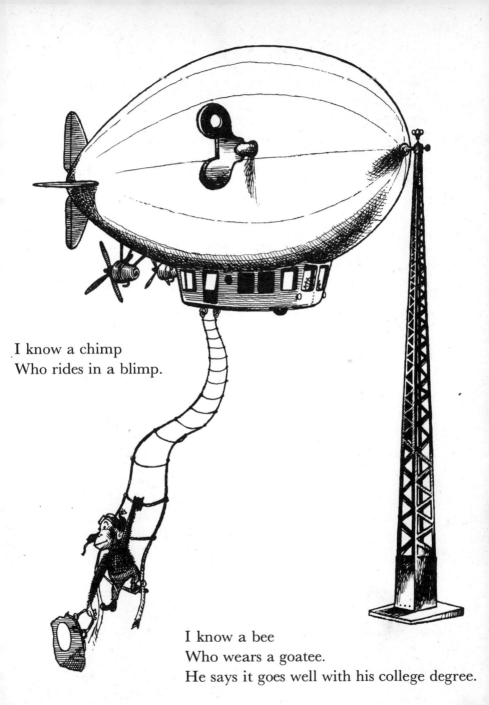

I know a chimp
Who rides in a blimp.

I know a bee
Who wears a goatee.
He says it goes well with his college degree.

11

I know some ants
That dress up in pants.

I know a fly
That wears a bow tie.

I know a fawn
Who's developing brawn
By tending his garden and mowing his lawn.

I know a whale
That receives lots of mail.
He opens it up with a flick of his tail.

13

I know a bear
Who shampoos his hair.

I know a sardine
Whose name is Eileen.
She likes to be seen in her new limousine.

I know a mule
Who skates to school.

I know a pig
Who wears a blond wig.

It sometimes falls off when he dances a jig.

I know a hyena
Who's fond of farina.

I wish you'd remind me to bring them around.
  We'd all sit about on the floor or the ground,
  And talk about this and talk about that
Until we had had a Very Nice Chat.
We might try to see if we can't agree
On whether there's too much salt in the sea
And whether it's right for a red-headed ape
To go to school in a green satin cape.

There are lots of dogs in Oddity Land
But, as you will find, they are differently planned.
They are rather hard to duplicate,
As you'll understand when you hear me state:

I know a Great Dane
Who was terribly plain,
So he grew a mustache and a lion-like mane.

I know a hound
Who often is found
At the carnival riding the merry-go-round.

I know a chow
Who is learning to bow.
He works in a palace and has to know how.

I know a retriever
Who romps with a beaver—
When tired they sit and recite "Danny Deever."

17

I know a Pom
Who went to a prom.
She wore her best dress that was made by her mom.

I know a schnauzer
Who answers to Towser.
He's fond of the bookshops and known as a browser.

I know a poodle
Who loves to doodle.

I know a griffon
Who always is tiffin',
Though often the other dog gives him a biffin'.
(My best dictionary has "biffing" right in it,
Or I would erase it, I would, in a minute.)

I know a spaniel whose front name is Daniel,
   He entered a Lion's Den
To prove he was fearless, but soon he was earless
   And never went back again.

He said, "If a spaniel whose front name is Daniel
   Would enter a Lion's Lair,
By far the best way is to pick out a day
   When he knows that the lion's not there."

I know a Peke
Who speaks Spanish and Greek,
Italian, Hungarian, French, Portuguese,
And every known language excepting Chinese.

I know a pug
Whose friends call him Mug.
An Indian taught him to bark the word "Ugh!"

I know a setter
Who says, "Donnerwetter!"
As well as a dachshund and possibly better.

I know a Maltese
Who shakes off his fleas
By means of a steady and violent sneeze.

I know a cocker who uses the knocker
    Whenever he comes to call.
He stands on a chair that we always leave there
    Because he's so terribly small.

There are birds, of course, in Oddity Land
But, as you have guessed, they are differently planned,
A fact that you'll be arriving at
When you read these little announcements that:

I know a bobwhite
Who's so very polite
He won't sing a note till he asks if he might.

I know a canary
Who works in a dairy.
She likes it because it is sunny and airy.

I know a flamingo
Who loves to play bingo.

I know a crow
Who's learning to sew.

I know a squab
Who likes corn on the cob.

I know a crane
Who pilots a plane.

I know a gander
Whose pet salamander
Is friends with a panda
Whose name is Amanda.
They play
Every day
On a near-by veranda.

I know a hawk
Who lives with an auk.
When not playing checkers they're out for a walk.

I know a goose who is friends with a moose,
  The largest of all the deer.
She likes to ride on his antlers wide
  And pretend the big creature to steer.

Her make-believe wheel she swings to the right
  When the moose goes trotting that way,
And many declare they're the happiest pair
  They ever have seen at play.

I know a macaque
Who lives in a shack
With some ducks who have offered to teach him to quack.

I know a jay
Who pulls a sleigh.
He claims he develops his muscles that way.

I know a pheasant
Whose ways are so pleasant—
On Christmas and birthdays he sends me a present.

I know an owl
Who uses a towel
To dry himself after it rains.
"I hate being wet," he explains.

I know a starling
Who does so much snarling
That only his mother believes he's a darling.

I know a tern
Who likes to eat fern,
But he much prefers frankfurters served in an urn.

I know a hen that quacks like a duck,
Especially when she's in mud and muck.
When I asked her why, her only reply
Was, "How many stars are there up in the sky?"

I know a duck that clucks like a hen,
She does it all day and at night again.
When I asked her why, her only reply
Was, "Some like pudding and some like pie."

I know a coot
Who smokes a cheroot.
He thinks he's an owl

                    and he's learning to hoot.

I know a loon
Who plays the bassoon
While a chorus of zebras surround him and croon.

I know a vulture
Who's gone in for culture.

I know a finch
Who loves to pinch.
He does it real hard and he laughs when you flinch.

I know a martin
Who dresses in tartan,
A pattern she looks decidedly smart in.

I know a swan
Who's expression's been wan
Since the day she discovered her feathers were gone.

I know a raven who sounds like a knave in
Proclaiming that he is the raven we know
From the poem by Poe.
I don't think it's so.

I know a partridge
Who swallowed a cartridge
And didn't, poor lad,
Realize that he had.
The day he exploded
He mournfully said
With a shake of his head,
"I had no idea I was loaded!"

As you know, I'm sure, in Oddity Land
  The fish are also differently planned,
  From the horse-tailed tarpon that lives on land
To the carp with no head and a couple of tails
And a skin of gold spangles instead of scales,
And the catfish that wears a derby hat—
So you will not find it surprising that . . .

I know a herring
Who starts people staring
By swinging a cane as he goes for an airing.

I know a sardine
Who runs a canteen.
The soldiers all say that he keeps the place clean.

I know a shad
Who's a college grad.
He's a pretty good speller and knows how to add.

I know a pike
Who travels by bike.

I know a smelt
Who always has felt
A fish is much tidier wearing a belt.

There's another shad
Who says, "Egad,"
Though the term is forbidden by his dad,
Who foolishly thinks it means something bad.

I know a flounder
Who couldn't be rounder.
One day he swallowed
A basketball
But he doesn't seem
To mind it at all.

I know a grampus
That lives on a campus,

And then there's another that dwells in the pampas.

I know a trout
Who is getting real stout,
And he's puzzled because he eats nothing but kraut.

I know a scrod
Who sleeps on the sod.
He prefers it to water. Decidedly odd!

I know a dolphin
Who loves to go golfin'.

I know a perch
Who lives in a birch.
He's writing a tree book and doing research.

I know a carp
Who plays a harp.

And now I'll give you a big assortment
  (From insects to animals) whose deportment
  Is what one expects in Oddity Land
Where everything is peculiarly planned,
Where the mammals don't act as they do in the zoo
And even the sprites take a different view
Of the things that fairies and pixies should do,
Where black may be white and pink may be brown,
And everything's joyously upside down,
Where the year begins with the month of May,
Where horses eat steaks and people eat hay . . .

But why go on? Let us meet a few
Of this oddly assorted unusual crew:

I know seven mice
That go skating on ice.
One doesn't like it and six think it's nice.

I know a moth
Who grew tired of cloth,
And now he eats nothing but crackers and broth.

I know a lemming
Who's taken up hemming.

I know a lynx
Who eats roses and pinks—
They taste a lot better than daisies, he thinks.

I know a sable
Remarkably able
At drawing cartoons
With clever "balloons."
He does his best work on a Chippendale table.

I know a stag
Who lives on a crag
Where he and a squirrel play leapfrog and tag.

I know a bull
Whose coat is pure wool.
It makes him feel sheepish
And Little Bo-Peepish.

I know an oyster whose friends are awhirl.
He discovered a person inside of a pearl.

I know a dragon
Whose home is a wagon.
He often drinks milk from a ten-gallon flagon.

    I know a mule
    Who likes to play pool.

    I know a goat
    Who wears a tweed coat
    And a fancy silk muffler encircling his throat.

    I know a weasel
    Who paints at an easel.
    I'm told his best painting is "Child with One Measle."

I know a ghost
Whose favorite boast
Is that he once haunted a thousand-mile coast.

I know a camel who paints the enamel
   Of all his teeth a bright blue.
When I asked him why, he declared with a sigh,
   "I'd tell you if only I knew!"

I know a sloth
Who once took an oath
To grow a mustache and it's now quite a growth.

I know a deer who's a grenadier
   And lives in a soldier suit.
He told me, "I like to parade and to hike,
   And I also love to salute."

I know a tabby
Who's terribly gabby.
Her name is Lenore but her friends call her Blabby.

I know a newt
Who loves to toot
His favorite tunes on his grandfather's flute.

I know a squirrel who caused both his parents
   To utter some peevish "tut-tuts"
By pushing away his dinner one day
   And saying, "I'm tired of nuts."

I know a flea with a wobbly knee
   Which he got in a football game.
I suggested a sport of a quieter sort
   But he thought it was much too tame.

I know a ram
Who loves biscuits and jam.

I know a bear
With a positive flair
For jumping up high
    and then walking on air.

I know a tapir
Whose favorite caper
Is blowing on windows until there's a vapor.

I know a cow who says, "How, now?"
  And "How have you been, no doubt?"
And "How's your hay?" and "Going my way?"
  And "Isn't it pleasant out?"

She likes to plow, this unusual cow.
  She was stopped by a horse one day,
Who showed her how and gave her a plow,
  And now it's her form of play.

I know a fly
Who has a black eye.
When asked how he got it he merely says, "Fie!"

I know an old rabbit who's famed for his habit
    Of smoking a pipe after tea.
"It helps me to think," he explains with a wink,
    "And that's enough reason for me."

I know a possum who eats orange blossom
   And will not eat anything but.
They tried him on cheese and hummingbirds' knees
   But he brushed 'em aside with a "Tut!"

By a very rich pal he was sent out to Cal.
   (On a steamer or was it a train?)
Where he eats orange blossom, this very odd possum,
   In salads and dumplings—and plain.

I know a toad
Who likes pie à la mode.

I know a gopher who's known as a loafer,
   He's lazy as he can be.
He'll start a big hole and then hire a mole
   To finish the tunneling. See?

I know a shrew
Who plays with a mew,
A green-and-white smew,
And a big wanderoo.
Ask someone to tell you their meanings, please do.
They're all in the zoo.

           I know a mink
           With the silliest wink.

I know a young otter
Who's quite a good yachter.
His name, if you care, is J. Hannibal Potter.

I know a sheep who doesn't baa.
The same is true of her maa and paa.
They prefer to squeal the way pigs do,
Excepting when in the mood to moo.

        I know a rhino
        Who's turning albino.

I know an alpaca
Who's fond of tobacca.

I know a horse who says, "Perforce."
   He was once in a Shakespeare play
Called "Richard the Third," and he thinks that word
   Is a cultured thing to say.

I know a gazelle
Who runs a hotel,
And runs it, they tell me, remarkably well.

I know a monkey who brays like a donkey,
    And nobody really knows why.
When I asked him to say why he acted that way
    He said with a sad little sigh:

"I once knew a rat whose best friend was a cat
    But the reason he couldn't relate.
It's the same way with me, and the reason must be
    It's probably something I ate."

I know a shote
Who wears a frock coat.

Examine the drawing and you will note
That his sister is wearing a petticoat.

I know a seal
Who plays with an eel.

I know a hog that croaks like a frog.
I know a frog that "oinks" like a hog.

I know a yak
Who swallowed a tack.
I tickled him hard and he coughed it right back.

I know a llama
Who's fond of the drama.
She often is taken by poppa and momma.

I know a grizzly
Who keeps her hair frizzly.

I know a loris
Whose front name is Boris.
He has a nice voice and he sings in a chorus.

I know a snail
Who plays chess with a quail.

I know a sprite
Six inches in height
Who tripped up a bandit and put him to flight.

I know a giraffe who is less than half
  The size that he ought to be.
When I wanted to know what had shortened him so
  He explained it as follows to me:

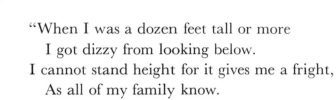

"When I was a dozen feet tall or more
  I got dizzy from looking below.
I cannot stand height for it gives me a fright,
  As all of my family know.

"Somewhere they had read of shortening bread
  And they got me a batch to try,
And it shortened me fast, so I'm finished at last
  With standing too high in the sky."

I know a cricket
That lives in a picket
That's part of a white picket fence.
When asked how he liked it he chirruped, "Immense!
It's a nice place to stay
With no rental to pay.
I think I was clever to pick it."

I need hardly say that in Oddity Land
  The people too are differently planned.
  The men and the women play with the toys,
And where does that leave the girls and boys?

Well, I know a girl of eight or nine
Who's said to be doing remarkably fine
As the principal of a public school,
A rather unusual thing as a rule,
But in Oddity Land it is nothing at all.

And I know a boy, and he's rather small,
Who runs a plant that makes automobiles.
He keeps so busy he eats all his meals
At his desk on which there are twenty phones
That connect him with all of the diff'rent zones
All over the world where he sells his cars.
The factory also makes chocolate bars,
They give you ten with each car you buy,
And they also give you a hot mince pie.

MUSICIAN No. 552

And I know a baby in Oddity Land
Who conducts what I'm sure is the world's biggest band.
There are ninety-nine fiddles and masses and masses
Of clarinets, drums and assorted brasses—

MUSICIAN Nº 561

Five hundred and sixty-two pieces in all,
Arrayed in a beautiful music hall,
And the infant-conductor is two feet tall!

I know a pilot
Whose airplane is vi'let,
It matches the blooms where he lives on an islet.

I know a king
Who's a jolly old thing,
To amuse you he'll dance, play piano or sing.

I know a shepherd who uses a leopard
  In tending his flock on the range.
Since sheep are so mild and leopards so wild
  I thought it was all rather strange.

He chuckled, that shepherd, and told me, "That leopard
  Is safer than dogs, I have found.
He hasn't a tooth in his head, that's the truth,
  And he knows the best stories around."

I know a knight
Whose armor's so tight
He keeps saying "Ouch!" and I understand quite.

I know a young shah
Who never says "Ah!"
When asked by his doctor, instead he says "Bah!"
(This breach of good manners is troubling his ma.)

I know a man
Who is made of rattan.
He creaks when he sits, so he stands all he can.

I know a witch
Who fell in a ditch
When the wind caught her broomstick and caused it to pitch.

I know a barber
Whose shop's in an arbor
A mile and a quarter from Oddity Harbor.
He caters to goats who have beards to their knees,
For his favorite hobby is trimming goatees.

I know a plumber who's also a drummer.
He never forgets his sticks.
He does a rat-tat wherever he's at
And whatever there is to fix.

If a pipe's to be mended he'll rattle a tune
On the side of the same before starting,
And when he's all done he considers it fun
To drum out "Retreat" in departing.

AND

FINALLY . . .

It's time that I stopped but I love to chatter,
So I'll add a few lines of this silly patter
To show that I know that there lives in a willow
A hippo who sleeps on a very large pillow.

And I know an elephant built with three trunks
And some lovely peacocks that live with skunks.
And I know a cat who wears a high hat,
A turtle-neck sweater and silken cravat.

And I know a salmon that lives on land
And a midget rhino as big as your hand.
And I know a Scottie who really speaks Scotch,
A gorilla who uses a clock as a watch
(It's strapped to his wrist and it's funny to see).
And I know a bee who is learning to ski,
And an Irish setter that speaks with a brogue,
He does it to start people laughing, the rogue!

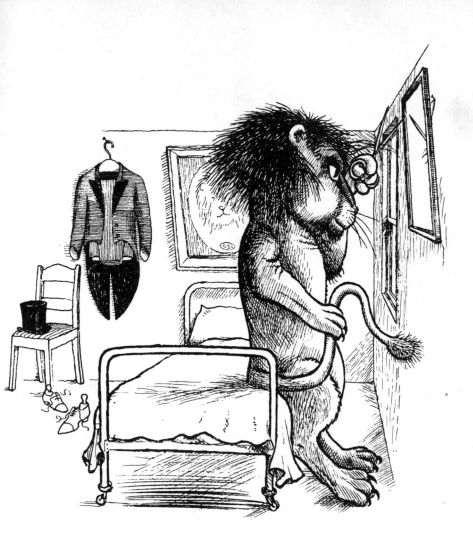

And I know a lion who trims his mane
And the tuft of his tail, I hear he is vain.

And I know a sailfish who offered his sail
To a man in a boat who was caught in a gale.
And I know a sweet little lisping panther,
When questioned he can't give a very clear anther.

And I know a tiger with dimpled cheeks
But I'm not deceived by his smile when he speaks.
And I know a lizard who's fond of a blizzard,
He likes to eat snow, says it cools off his gizzard.

I could continue like this forever
But if I did
            you would go to bed
                        NEVER,

    So I'll let these verses do for now
    As I say good-bye with my fanciest bow.